McGRAW-HILL READING

Consulting Authors

Barbara Coulter, Frankie Dungan, Joseph B. Rubin,
Carl B. Smith, Shirley Wright

Contributors

The Princeton Review, Time Magazine

The Princeton Review is not
affiliated with Princeton
University or ETS.

McGraw-Hill School Division

A Division of The McGraw-Hill Companies

McGraw-Hill School Division
Two Penn Plaza
New York, New York 10121

Printed in the United States of America

ISBN 0-02-184719-3/1, Book 3
 2 3 4 5 6 7 8 9 043/071 04 03 02 01 00

Macmillan/McGraw-Hill Edition

LYX
1.00-4
Mcg
bk. 3

McGRAW-HILL READING

Authors

DISCARDED

James Flood

Jan E. Hasbrouck

James V. Hoffman

Diane Lapp

Angela Shelf Medearis

Scott Paris

Steven Stahl

Josefina Villamil Tinajero

Karen D. Wood

 McGraw-Hill
School Division

New York   Farmington

Stories to Tell

Something About Me 6
An Anonymous Poem

Circus Stunts 8
A Phonics Rhyme

Stan's Stunt 10
A Humorous Story by Lynn Plourde
illustrated by Pam Levy

    Story Questions and Activities 34

    Study Skills: Diagram of a Skunk 36

        LANGUAGE ARTS/SCIENCE CONNECTION

    TAAS

    Test Power 37

Drips! Drops! 38
A Phonics Rhyme

Greg's Mask 40
Realistic Fiction by Ann McGovern
illustrated by Winky Adam

    Story Questions and Activities 64

    Study Skills: Diagram of an Art Center 66

        ART/SOCIAL STUDIES CONNECTION

    TAAS

    Test Power 67

Lunch Munch..**68**
A Phonics Rhyme

Sam's Song..**70**
A Fantasy Story by Alyssa Satin Capucilli
illustrated by Melissa Iwai
    Story Questions and Activities **94**
    Study Skills: Diagram of Owl Sizes...................**96**
TAAS   SCIENCE/SOCIAL STUDIES/MATH CONNECTION
✪ **Test Power** **97**

Snake's Trip...............................**98**
A Phonics Rhyme

Snakes.......................................**100**
A Nonfiction Article by Frances Minters
    Story Questions and Activities......................**122**
    Study Skills: Diagram of Snake Lengths..........**124**
TAAS   SCIENCE/MATH CONNECTION
✪ **Test Power** **125**

Camp Out................................**126**
A Phonics Rhyme

TIME FOR KIDS **Let's Camp Out!**................**128**
A Story from the Editors of TIME FOR KIDS
    Story Questions and Activities......................**136**
    Study Skills: Diagram of a Tent......................**138**
TAAS   SOCIAL STUDIES CONNECTION
✪ **Test Power** **139**

You're an Author Now **140**
A Poem by Kalli Dakos

Glossary **142**

READ TOGETHER

Stories to Tell

Something About Me

There's something about me
That I'm knowing.
There's something about me
That isn't showing.

I'm growing!

Anonymous

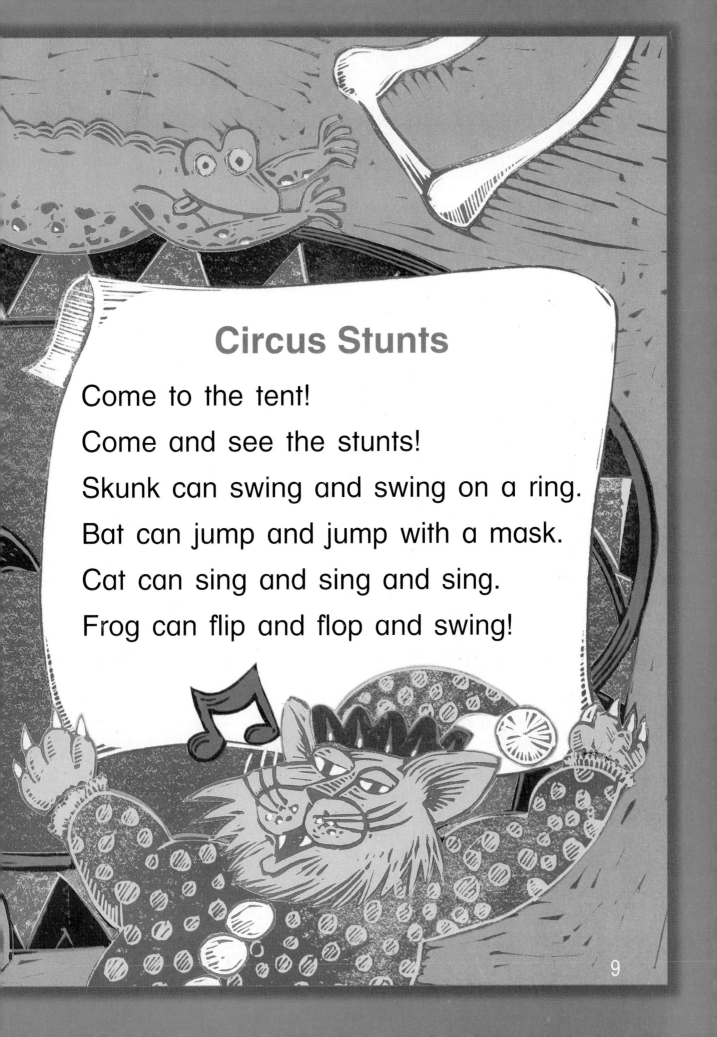

Circus Stunts

Come to the tent!

Come and see the stunts!

Skunk can swing and swing on a ring.

Bat can jump and jump with a mask.

Cat can sing and sing and sing.

Frog can flip and flop and swing!

Meet Lynn Plourde

Lynn Plourde lives in Maine. She has written many books for children. She also helps school children who have trouble speaking. She thinks both of her jobs are a lot of fun.

Meet Pamela R. Levy

When Pamela R. Levy was little she liked to draw. She did not think about becoming an artist until she went to college. Today she is the illustrator of many children's books. She also likes to dance, read, and garden.

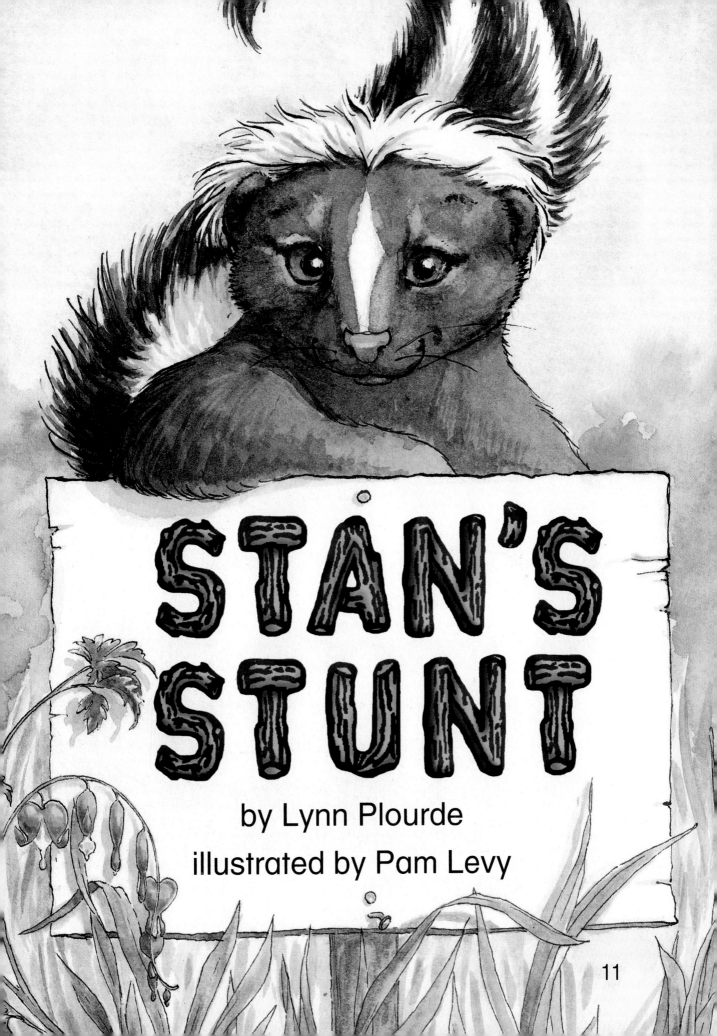

STAN'S STUNT

by Lynn Plourde

illustrated by Pam Levy

"I can do a stunt," said Stan the Skunk.

"What is a stunt?" asked Stan's pals.

"A stunt is a good trick!" said Stan.

Up went Stan's tail.

"No! Stop! Stop!" yelled Stan's pals.

"Look at *my* stunt," said Owl.
Up and down went Owl's lids.

Owl's lids went wink blink.

Then his lids went blink wink.

"Stan, try Owl's stunt," said Stan's pals.

"I like Owl's stunt," said Stan.

"And I can do his stunt," said Stan.

Stan went wink blink.

Then Stan went blink wink.

"But I would like to do *my* stunt,"
said Stan.
Up went Stan's tail again.
"No! Stop! Stop!" yelled Stan's pals.

"Take a look at *my* stunt," said Frog.
Up and down went Frog's legs.

Frog went jump bump.

Then Frog went bump jump.

"Stan, try Frog's stunt," said Stan's pals.

"I like Frog's stunt," said Stan.

"And I can do his stunt," said Stan.

Stan went jump bump.

Then Stan went bump jump.

"But I would like to do *my* stunt,"
said Stan.

Up went Stan's tail again.

"No! Stop! Stop!" yelled Stan's pals.

"Take a look at *my* stunt," said Bat.

Upside down went Bat.

Bat went flip flop.

Then Bat went flop flip.

"Stan, try Bat's stunt," said Stan's pals.

"I like Bat's stunt," said Stan.

"And I can do his stunt," said Stan.

Stan went flip flop.

Then Stan went flop flip.

"Do not fall!" yelled Stan's pals.

"Now I will do *my* stunt," said Stan.

Up went Stan's tail again.

Stan's pals had run out of stunts.

Stan's pals held their noses.

"Do it!" said Stan's pals.

"Do your stunt."

And Stan did.

Back and forth went Stan's tail.

Stan went wiggle waggle.

Stan wagged and wagged his tail.
Stan's pals sniffed and sniffed.
But they did not smell a thing.

"What a good stunt!" said Stan's pals.

"Will you try *my* stunt now?" asked Stan.

"Yes! Yes!" said Stan's pals.

Stan and his pals went waggle wiggle.
Then Stan and his pals went giggle
giggle.

1. What does Owl do?

2. Why did Stan's pals yell, "Stop!"?

3. What other stunts could the animals do?

4. Tell the story in your own words.

5. Name animals you have read about.

Write About a Stunt

Draw yourself doing a stunt.

Tell about the stunt.

Then write about it.

I like to do cartwheels.

Make a Forest Mural

Draw a picture of a forest.

Name an animal that lives in the forest.

Draw a picture of this animal.

Glue your picture in the forest.

Find Out More

Have you ever seen a skunk?

Find out more about this animal.

Share what you learn.

Skunk

This diagram shows the parts of a skunk.

tail

body

head

paw

nose   eyes

claws

Look at the Diagram

1 What color is the skunk's tail?

2 Count the claws on a paw.

Flo the Pig

Flo is a pink pig.

She lives on a farm in a pigpen.

There are many other pigs.

Flo likes to play games.

Her favorite game is piggyback.

When Flo plays, she likes to win.

But win or lose, Flo has fun.

Where does this story take place?

○ In the forest

○ On a farm

Look for clues in the story to help answer the question.

Drips! Drops!

Drip, drop, it is wet.

The drops are small and big.

Brett and Glen slip and slop

As they play and dig.

Drip, drop, it is wet.

The drops are big and loud.

Brett and Glen wait for the sun

To drag away the cloud.

Meet Ann McGovern

When Ann McGovern was little, she was so shy that she never raised her hand in class. "I became a writer to express feelings that I couldn't speak about," she says. McGovern is now the author of almost 60 children's books.

Meet Winky Adam

Winky Adam says, "I knew I wanted to create children's books since I was in the third grade." Today, she writes and illustrates children's books.

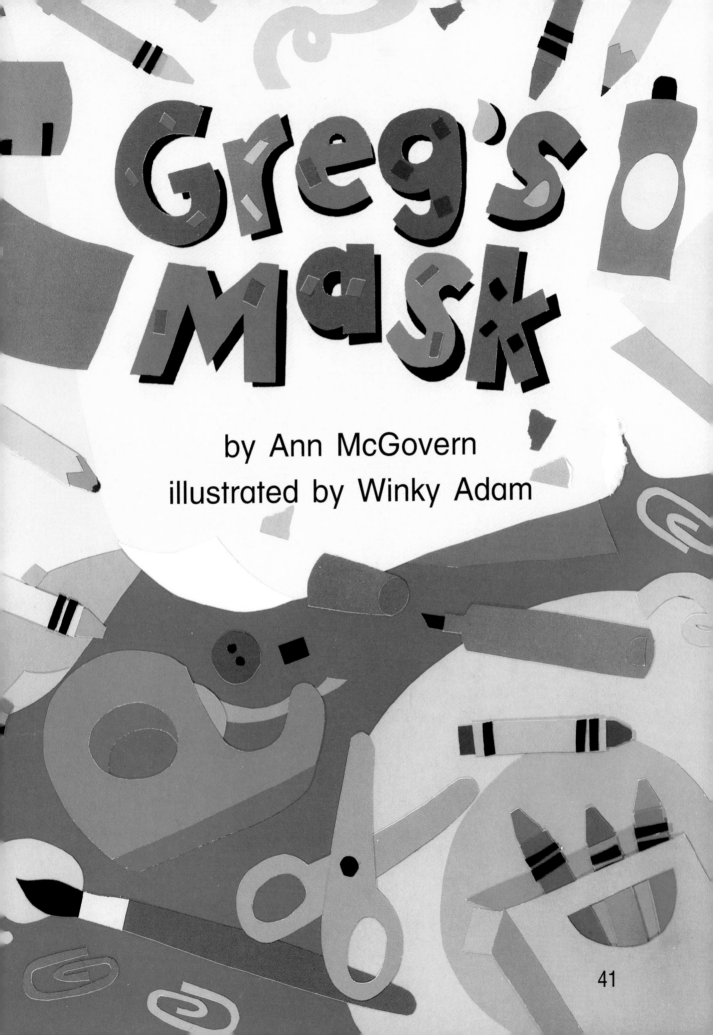

Greg's Mask

by Ann McGovern

illustrated by Winky Adam

Greg's class was putting on a skit.
Greg had to make a mask for it.

Greg sang as he worked.
"Snip it here.
Clip it there.
Clip. Snip. Snip. Clip."

"Drip a drop of this.
Drop a glob of that.
Drip. Drop. Drop. Drip."

"Rip it here.
Nip it there.
Rip. Nip. Nip. Rip."

"Twist it here.
Tape it there.
Twist. Tape. Tape. Twist."

Greg's mask was done.
He put it on.

47

Greg went to see his sister.
"Do you like my new mask?"
he asked Tam.

48

Tam was having a bad day.
"I do not want to look at
any old mask," she said.

Greg felt very sad. "My new mask is not any good," he said. And he tossed it into the trash.

Greg was still mad at Tam the next day. He left before her.

It was time for the skit.
"Where is your mask?" Miss Wills
asked Greg. But Greg did not have it.

Just then Tam ran into Greg's class.
"Greg, you forgot your mask!" she yelled.

Then Tam said, "Do not be mad at me. I take back what I said. Your mask is good!"

Greg put on his mask. He was ready for the skit.

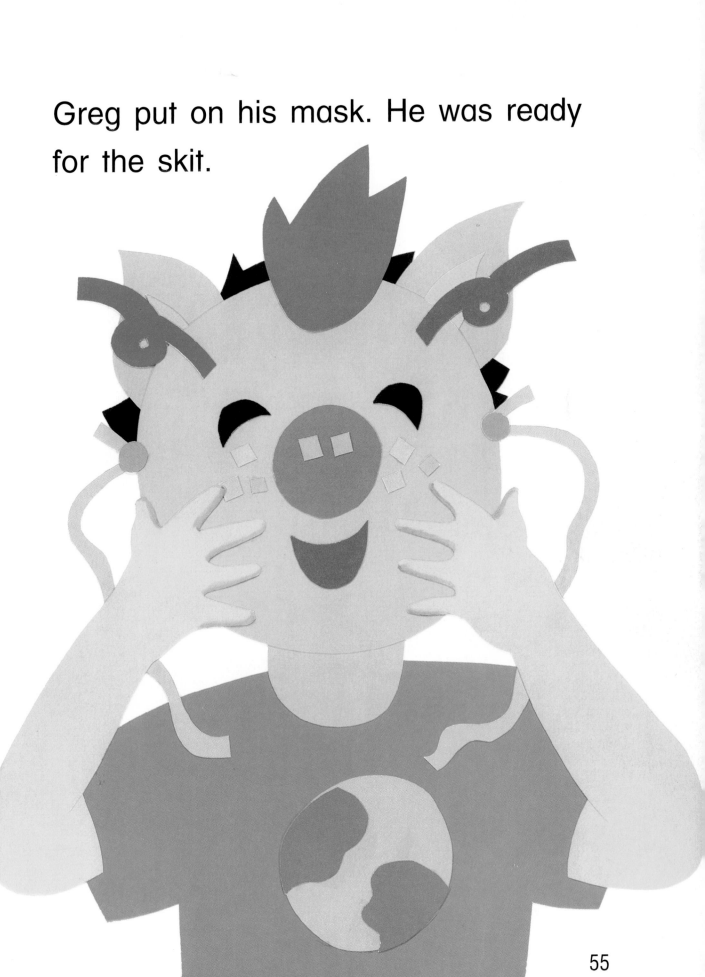

There were masks of a duck, a frog, a fish, a dog, a mouse, and a cat. But Tam said Greg's mask was the best!

When Tam got home, she asked Greg, "Will you help me make a mask for *my* class skit?"

Greg and Tam sang.

"Snip it here.

Clip it there.

Clip. Snip. Snip. Clip."

"Drip a drop of this.
Drop a glob of that.
Drip. Drop. Drop. Drip."

"Rip it here. Nip it there.
Rip. Nip. Nip. Rip.
Twist it here. Tape it there.
Twist. Tape. Tape. Twist."

Tam's mask was done. She put it on.
"What a good mask!" Greg said.

"That was fun!" said Greg.

"I just may do this when I grow up!"

Story Questions & Activities

1 How did Greg make his mask?

2 Why did Tam bring the pig mask to Greg?

3 What was the class skit about?

4 Tell the story in your own words.

5 How is Greg like Max the Cat?

Make a Poster

Draw a picture about Greg's skit.

Write a title for it.

Tell where the skit will be.

Tell when the skit will be.

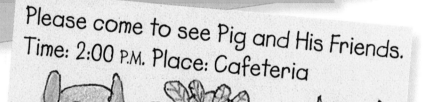

Please come to see Pig and His Friends.
Time: 2:00 P.M. Place: Cafeteria

Make a Mask

Use a paper plate.

Make an animal mask.

Then use your mask for a class skit.

What will it be about?

Find Out More

There are many kinds of masks.

Look for pictures of masks.

What are they made of?

Art Center

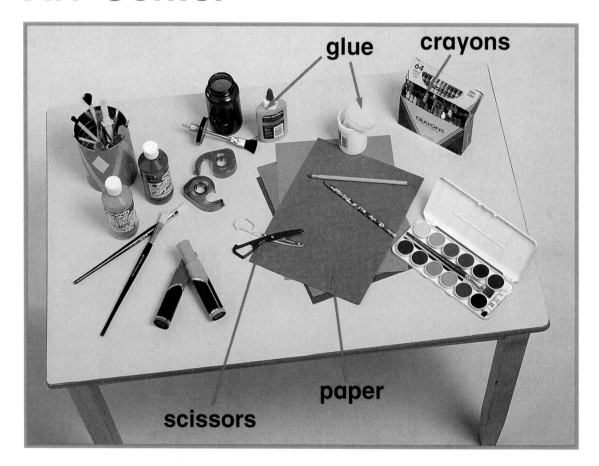

glue   crayons

paper

scissors

Look at the Art Center

❶ What do you use to cut?

❷ Tell what you would do with glue.

Bart's House of Snow

Bart got out of bed.

He went out to play in the yard.

He made a house in the snow.

Bart showed it to his sister.

At first, she did not like it.

But then, they started to play.

They played outside for a long time.

Then, they went in to have lunch.

Where does this story take place?

○ At Bart's school

○ In Bart's yard

Read the story again if the question seems too hard.

67

Lunch Munch

Hank sits up on top

When we have lunch.

Mom gives him lots

To chomp and crunch.

He spills his drink.

Chomp, chomp, crunch, munch.

Hank learns to chew

Each bit and bunch.

Meet Alyssa Satin Capucilli

Alyssa Satin Capucilli began writing stories when she was just a little girl. When Capucilli grew up and had children, she knew that she wanted a career writing for children. "I get ideas from the wonderful memories of my own family and from things that I care about," she says.

Meet Melissa Iwai

Melissa Iwai has been drawing since she was little. By the time she was nine, she was making books for herself. She says, "I always wanted to illustrate children's books." And now she does.

Sam's Song

by Alyssa Satin Capucilli

illustrated by Melissa Iwai

The owls sat on their branch.
They watched the sun sink
down,

    down,

        down.

It was pitch black out.

Now they would sing.

"Whooooo!" sang Mom.

"Whooooo!" sang Pop.

Chuck could sing, too.

"Whooooo!" he sang out.

Then they sang together.
What a nice song it was!

One day there was a big fuss.

"What is it?" asked Chuck.

"It's a new chick!" said Mom.

"Let's call her Sam!" said Pop.

The owls sat on their branch again.
They watched the sun sink
down,
        down,
                down.

"Whooooo!" sang Mom.

"Whooooo!" sang Pop.

"Whooooo!" sang Chuck.

They looked at Sam.

But Sam didn't sing.
She just put her chin down
in her mom's wing.

"Why can't Sam sing?" asked Chuck.

"Now then," said Mom.

"Sam will sing when she wants to."

The owls sat on their branch again.

It was pitch black out.

Mom, Pop, and Chuck sang.

But Sam still couldn't sing.

Sam's chest sank.

"Why can't I sing?" she asked.

Pop put his wing around Sam.

"Let's go back to the nest," he said.

Sam wouldn't eat or drink.

She just went to bed.

Then she saw a small star wink at her.

"I can wish on it," Sam said.

"Whoo!"

"What was that?" asked Mom.

"Whoo!"

It was Sam!

"You can sing, Sam!" they said.

"But I can't sing like you," said Sam.

"My song is much too small."

"We'll see about that," said Pop.

"Let's go out together."

Whish! Whish!

"What was that?" asked Sam.

"That was a firefly," said Pop.

"That was small," said Sam.

Plink! Plunk!

"What was that?" asked Sam.

"That was a nut," said Mom.

"That was small, too," said Sam.

Crunch! Crunch!

"What was that?" asked Sam.

"I think it's a mouse," said Chuck.

"A mouse is small, too," said Sam.

The owls sat on their branch.

Mom, Pop, and Chuck sang together.

Sam began to sing.

She saw her star wink at her.

"Whoo!" sang Sam.

It was not big. It was small.

But it was hers!

The owls sang one last song
together. Now Sam sang with them.
It was their best song yet!

Story Questions & Activities

1 How is Sam's song different from the others?

2 Who is Chuck?

3 How will Sam's song sound when she is bigger?

4 What is this story mostly about?

5 What might Stan say to Sam?

Draw a Picture

Whish, crunch, plunk are sound words.
What do you think of when you hear them?
Draw pictures of what you hear.

Put on a Skit

Pick parts to play from
"Sam's Song."

Who will be Sam?

Who will be the mouse?

Use sound words in your skit.

Make your voices
soft and loud.

Find Out More

What songs do you like?

Go to the school library.

Find words to songs you like.

If you can, find tapes of the songs.

Share them with your class.

Play your tape.

Or, sing your song.

Owls

Owls are different sizes.

screech owl

elf owl

barn owl

great horned owl

Look at the Owls

1. Which owl is the biggest?

2. Which owl is smaller than the screech owl?

Big Ball, Small Ball

Look at these balls.
The baseball is a small ball.
The golf ball is smaller.
The marble is the smallest.

Look at these large balls.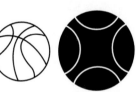
The basketball is large.
The kickball is larger.
The beach ball is the largest.

What is smaller than a baseball?

○ A marble

○ A basketball

For each answer choice, ask yourself if it answers the question.

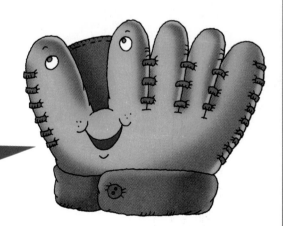

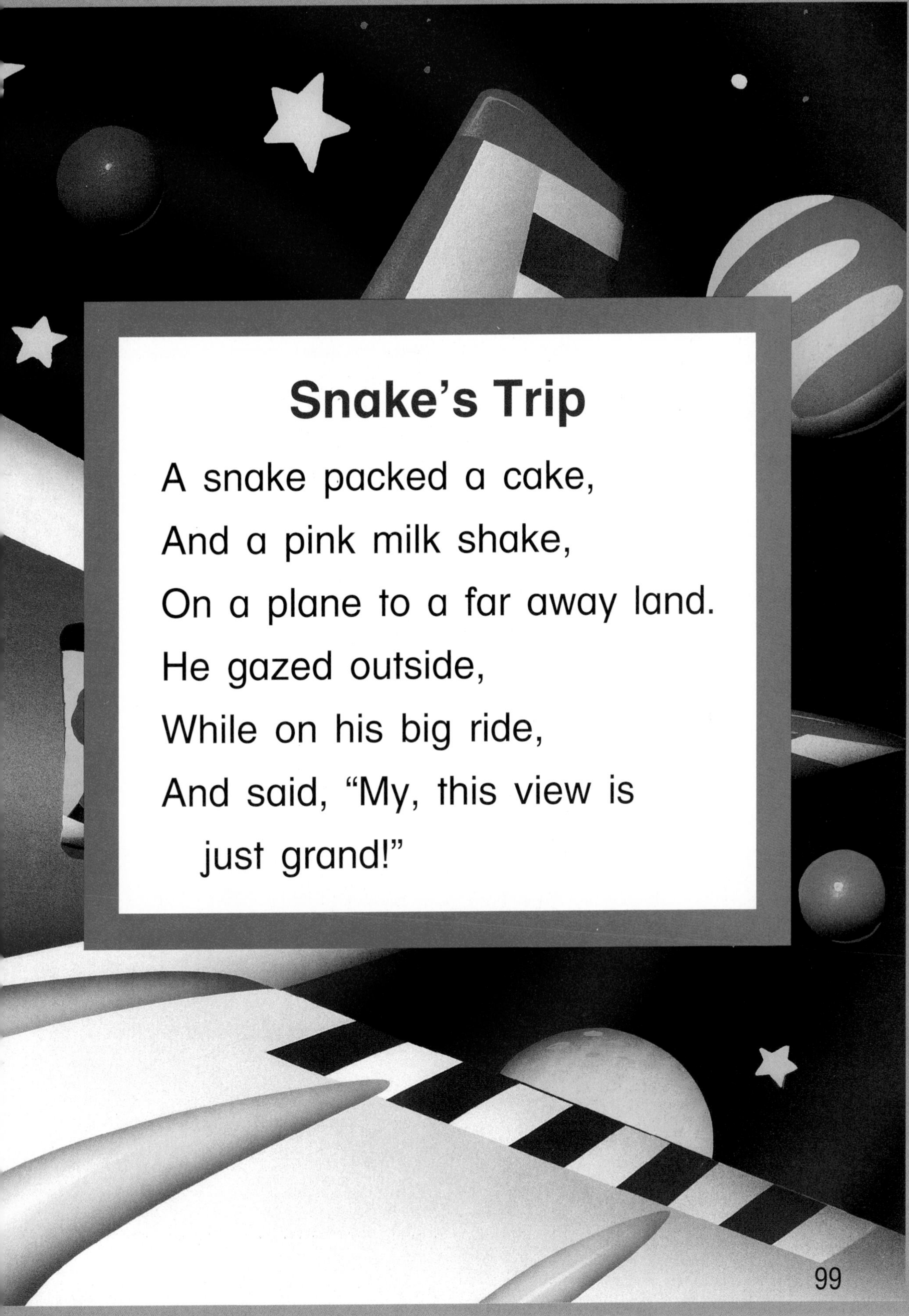

Snake's Trip

A snake packed a cake,

And a pink milk shake,

On a plane to a far away land.

He gazed outside,

While on his big ride,

And said, "My, this view is

just grand!"

Meet Frances Minters

Frances Minters has worked as a teacher and book editor. "But I have always wanted to be a writer," she says. "I am glad that I am one now." She has written *Cinder-Elly* and *Sleepless Beauty.* Minters lives in Florida with her husband, Arthur, and their cat, Lenny. "Lenny has never seen a snake, but he loves lizards," she says.

Snakes

by Frances Minters

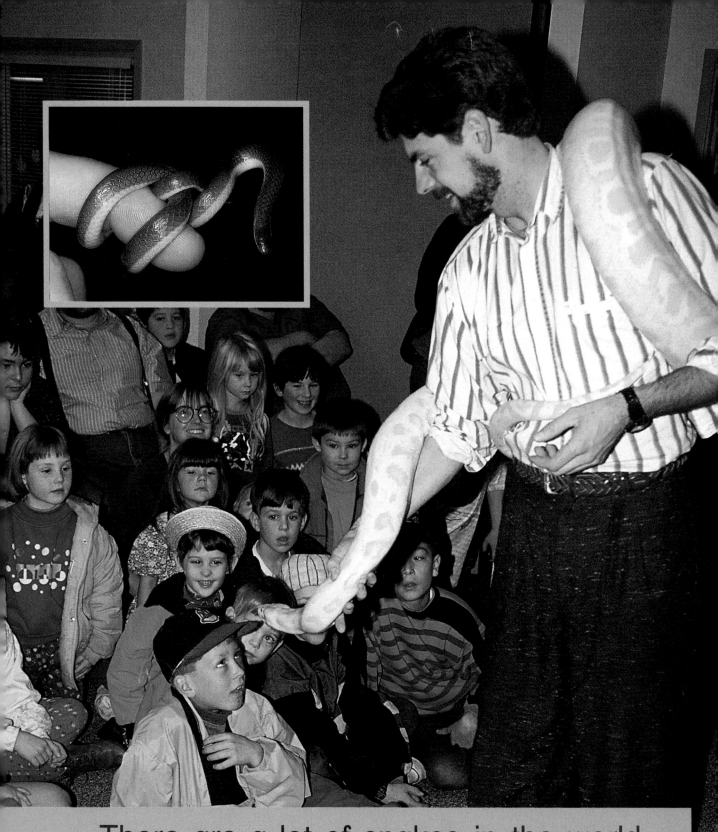

There are a lot of snakes in the world.
There are big snakes and small snakes.

You can find snakes in hot lands
and in damp lands.

Most of the snakes that you see will not harm you.

But some snakes can.
So be safe!

Do you know how a snake eats?
Look at that big lump in its body.
That big lump is a big rat!

A snake can make its mouth very big.
That is how it can eat such big things.

Can a snake run?
A snake has no legs. It can't run.

But a snake can move.

It can get where it wants to go.

Where can a snake be safe?
A snake can be safe under a rock
or in a log.

A snake can make a nest in the grass.
A snake can live in a lake or on a
big branch.

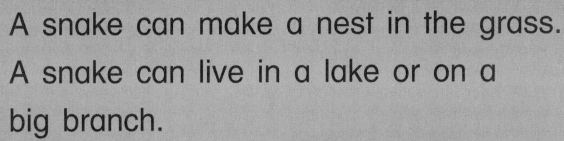

111

Do you know that a snake's skin is made of small scales?

A snake can grow a new skin under
its old skin. Then the old skin falls off.

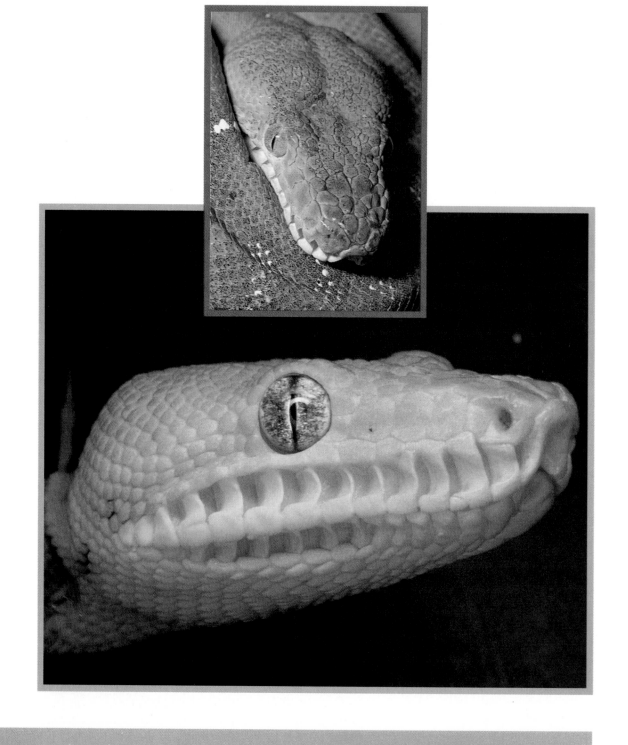

A snake has eyes, but it does not have lids. A snake has ears, but you cannot see them.

A snake can hiss. A snake's hiss
is like this: Sssss.

Do you know about baby snakes?

A baby snake has an egg tooth.
The snake uses it to get out of its shell.
When the snake is out of the shell,
its egg tooth falls out.

Baby snakes can get
their own food.

The small snakes will get big very fast.
They will get as big as their mom
and dad.

Would you like to have a snake as a pet? Tell why or why not!

1 What is a snake's skin made of?

2 Why might a snake hiss?

3 Are all snakes good pets? Why?

4 Name three snake facts.

5 Could a snake be in "Stan's Stunt"?

Write About a Snake

Find out about one snake.

Write two sentences about it.

Tell where it lives.

Tell about the food it eats.

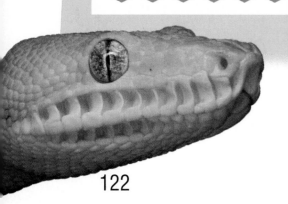

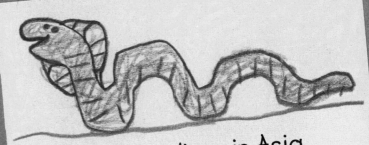

The cobra lives in Asia.
It eats frogs and fish.

122

A Big Hiss!

Draw a big snake.

Think about snakes.

What words remind you of snakes?

Share the words with your class.

Write the words

in your snake picture.

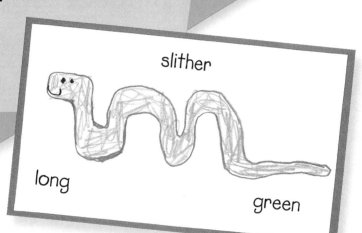

Find Out More

Choose a kind of snake from the story.

Find out one more fact about it.

Write down that fact.

Snake Lengths

Snakes are different lengths.

boa constrictor

sidewinder

anaconda

rattlesnake

Look at the Snakes

1 Which snakes are longer than the sidewinder? Point to them.

2 Which snakes are shorter than the anaconda? Point to them.

124

Sam and the Frog

Sam is a brown dog.

Jon is a green frog.

Sam is bigger than Jon.

Jon is just a small frog.

Sam has lots of fur.

Jon has no fur.

Of course not, he is a frog.

_____

Who has more fur?

○ Jon the frog

○ Sam the dog

Look in the story for clues.

Camp Out

Tramp, tramp, tramp down the track,

See our caps and big backpacks.

I am Chet and that is Jake,

We set up camp next to a lake.

Look at Jake fish in the lake!

He will get us a bass to bake.

Put up the tent and we are in.

It is night—when dreams begin.

TIME
FOR KIDS
SPECIAL REPORT

Let's Camp Out!

You can go on a trip.

Get your pack and let's go!

When you camp, you sleep in a tent.
Try to pick a good spot to put up your tent.

You can go on a hike.

Look around you for things like a nest.

You can use old sticks and twigs to make a fire. It can help you warm up.

Food tastes good when you
eat it outside.

You can sing songs together under the stars. Look for the Big Dipper!

Sleep well in your tent.

See you when the sun is up!

A story from the editors of *TIME FOR KIDS*.

135

1 What do you need for a campfire?

2 Where do people camp out?

3 What sounds do you hear camping?

4 Name three things you can do camping.

5 Which animals from "Stan's Stunt" might you see when you camp out?

Tell How to Do It

How do you roast marshmallows at a camp fire? Tell what you need. Tell how to roast them. Then draw a picture of yourself roasting them.

Play Stuck-in-the-Mud, a Camp Game

One person is IT. IT tags someone.

The person tagged stands still.

That person is stuck in the mud.

The game is over when IT tags everyone.

Then someone else can be IT.

Find Out More

Learn a camp song.
Share it with the class.

Diagram of a Tent

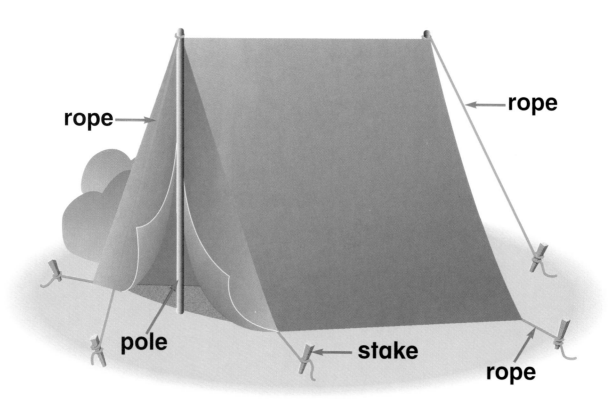

rope

rope

rope

pole

stake

Look at the Diagram

1 What holds the ropes in place?

2 How many poles are there?

Let's Camp Out

Let's camp here.

There are lots of trees.

And the woods are nice and quiet.

Let's put up the tent.

Make sure the door is closed.

We don't want to sleep with the bugs.

Now let's cook dinner.

After dinner, we can tell stories.

Where does this story take place?

○ In the woods

○ In a parking lot

Think about the story as you read it.

139

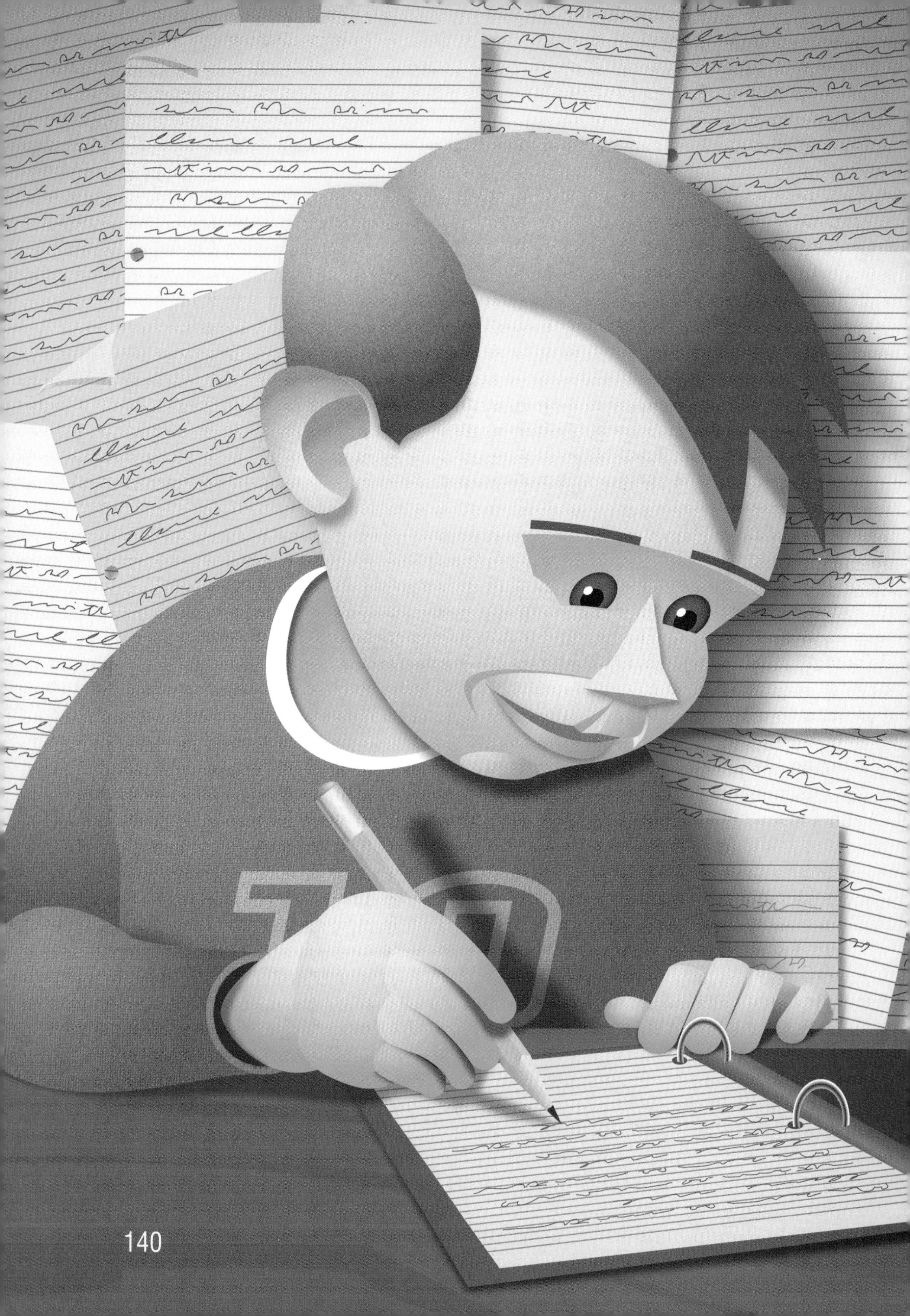

You're an Author Now

I'm writing,

I'm writing,

I'm writing in my book.

I'm writing,

I'm writing,

Oh, Teacher, come and look.

You're writing,

You're writing,

I'm glad you've learned how.

You're writing,

You're writing,

You're an author now.

by Kalli Dakos

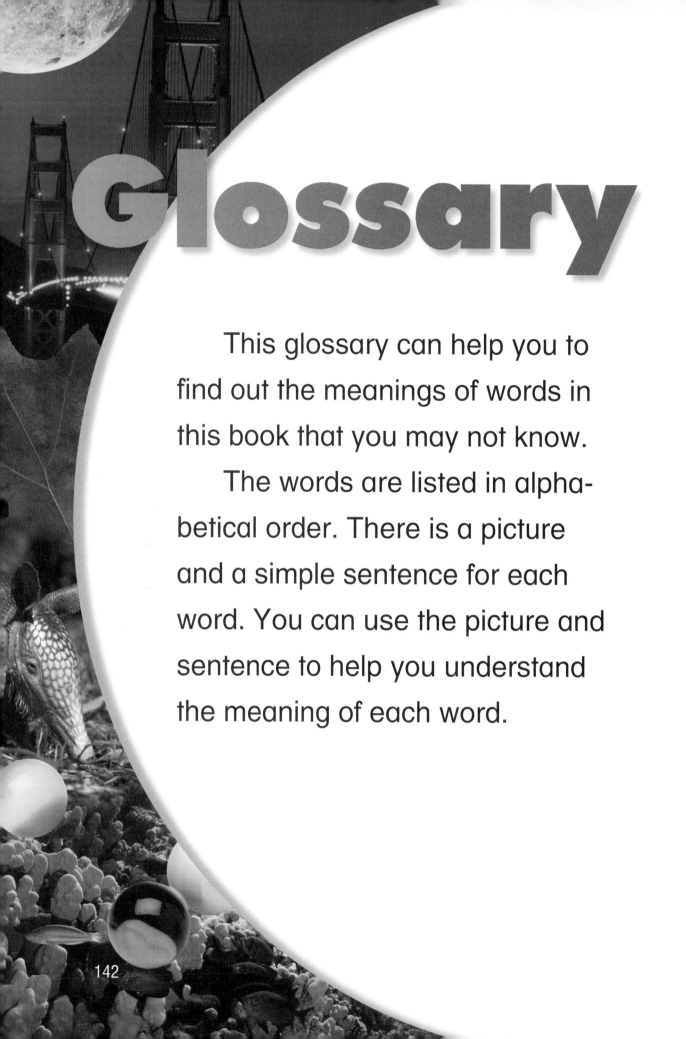

Glossary

This glossary can help you to find out the meanings of words in this book that you may not know.

The words are listed in alphabetical order. There is a picture and a simple sentence for each word. You can use the picture and sentence to help you understand the meaning of each word.

Sample Entry

Main Entry   **Sample Sentence**

Branch

A bird is sitting on the **branch.**

Another word for **branch** is *limb.*

Sample Picture

143

Baby

The **baby** drinks from a bottle.

Branch

A bird is sitting on the **branch.**

Another word for **branch** is *limb.*

Eyes

Len sees with his **eyes.**

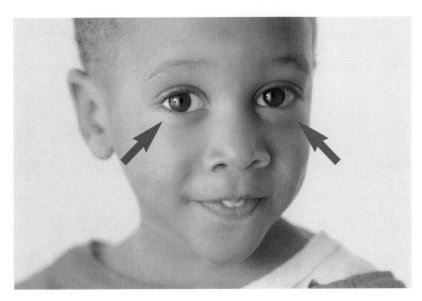

Fire

Be careful around the **fire.**

Frog

The **frog** can hop.

Mask

The **mask** covers Mark's face.

Nest

The **nest** is the bird's home.

Nut

The squirrel cracks the **nut** to eat it.

Star

Wish upon a **star.**

Sun

The **sun** is shining brightly.

Tail

This cat has a long **tail.**

Tape

Tape holds things in place.

Tent

It can be fun to sleep in a **tent.**

Tooth

When your **tooth** gets loose,
it falls out.

Trash

Throw your **trash** out.

Another word for **trash** is *garbage.*

Wink

You use your eye when you **wink.**

ACKNOWLEDGMENTS

The publisher gratefully acknowledges permission to reprint the following copyrighted material:

"Something About Me," anonymous from READ-ALOUD RHYMES FOR THE VERY YOUNG. Copyright © 1986 by Alfred A. Knopf, Inc. Illustrations copyright © 1986 by Marc Brown. Reprinted by permission of Alfred A. Knopf.

"You're an Author Now" by Kalli Dakos from MRS. COLE ON AN ONION ROLL AND OTHER SCHOOL POEMS. Text copyright © 1995 Kalli Dakos. Reprinted with the permission of Simon & Schuster Books for Young Readers, an imprint of Simon & Schuster Children's Publishing Division.

Illustration

Helen Ward, 6–7; Randall Enos, 8–9; Pam Levy, 10–33, 35cl; Daniel Del Valle, 34br, 35cr, 64b, 94b, 122br, 123cr; Bernard Adnet, 37, 125; Jean Hirashima, 38–39; Winky Adam, 40–63; 64tl, 64cr, 65c; Eldon Doty, 67–69, 139; Melissa Iwai, 70–93, 94cr, 95br; John Chinn, 96; Ken Bowser, 97br; Mas Miyamoto, 97tr; Bill Mayer, 98–99; Angela Adams, 124, 126–7; Nancy Tobin, 137; Menny Borovski, 138; John Hovell, 140–1; Felipe Galindo, 144, 150, 151; Peter Fasolino, 146, 149; John Carozza, 147.

Photography

100–101: cover Tony Stone Images/Tim Davis. 104–105: National Geographic Society Images Sales/Joseph Bailey. 116–117: Animals Animals/Earth Scenes/Zig Leszczynski. 120–121: Tony Stone Images/David J. Sams. 36: PhotoDisc, Inc./Photodisc. 70: b. Courtesy Melissa Iwai. t. Photo Credit: Kirchoff/Wohlberg, Inc.; 100: t. Courtesy of Frances Minters. 102: Animals, Animals/Earth Scenes/Michael Habicht. Photo Researchers, Inc./Stephen Collins; 103: Corbis Media/Michael and Patricia Fogden. 105: Animals Animals/Earth Scenes/Joe McDonald. Photo Researchers, Inc./F. Stuart Westmorland; 106: Animals Animals/Earth Scenes/Michael Fogden. 107: Animals Animals/Earth Scenes/Michael Fogden. 108: Tony Stone Images/Paul Chesley. 109: Animals Animals/Earth Scenes/OSF K. Atkinson. 110: Animals Animals/Earth Scenes/Michael Fogden. 111: Animals Animals/Earth Scenes/Joe McDonald. Corbis Media/David Northcolt; 112: Animals Animals/Earth Scenes/Zig Leszczynski. 113: Animals Animals/Earth Scenes/Zig Leszczynski. Animals Animals/Earth Scenes/Zig Leszczynski; 114: Animals Animals/Earth Scenes/Michael Fogden. Photo Researchers, Inc./Gregory Dimijian, MD; 115: Tony Stone Images/Tom Bean. 116: Animals Animals/Earth Scenes/Zig Leszczynski. 118: Animals Animals/Earth Scenes/Bill Beatty. 119: Animals Animals/Earth Scenes/Zig Leszczynski. 144: b. The Stock Market/U–AT. 145: b. Photo Network/J. Rothan/V. Jackson. t. The Stock Market/Steve Prezant; 146: b. Image Bank/G+J Images. 147: The Stock Market/Zefa Germany. 148: b. Tony Stone Images. t. Tony Stone Images/; 150: t. The Stock Market/David Stoecklein. 151: PhotoDisc. : Kirchoff/Wohlberg.